ALFRED'S BASIC GUITAR METHOD

BOOK 1

by ALFRED d'AUBERGE and MORTON MANUS

designed by ERNIE BARTH

Alfred Music CO. INC., NEW YORK

Getting Acquainted With Music

Musical sounds are indicated by symbols called NOTES. Their time value is determined by their color (white or black) and by stems and flags attached to the note:

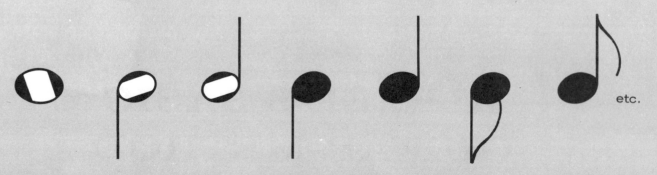

etc.

The notes are named after the first seven letters of the alphabet, endlessly repeated to embrace the entire range of musical sound. The name and pitch of the note is determined by its position on five horizontal lines, and the spaces between, called the . . .

Staff

―――――――――――――――――――5th LINE――――――――――――――――――――

4th SPACE

――――――――――――――――4th LINE――――――――――――――――

3rd SPACE

―――――――――――3rd LINE―――――――――――

2nd SPACE

――――――2nd LINE――――――

1st SPACE

――――1st LINE――――

NOTES ON THE LINES   NOTES IN THE SPACES

Because the five-line staff cannot contain all the notes of our musical system, other short lines are added above and below the staff, called . . .

Leger Lines

LEGER LINES ABOVE THE STAFF

LEGER LINES BELOW THE STAFF

During the evolution of musical notation, the staff had from 2 to 20 lines, and symbols were invented to locate certain lines and the pitch of the note on that line. These symbols were called . . .

Clefs

Music has three clefs, the C, F and G clefs. The entire range of the Guitar can be written in the G clef and is used exclusively in this book. Originally the Gothic letter G was used on a four-line staff to establish the pitch of G: ......

It grew into the modern ......

G

Comparative Note Values

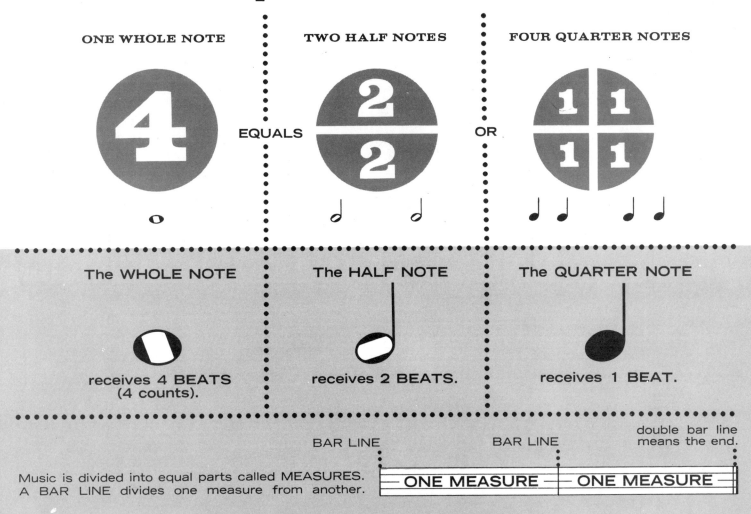

ONE WHOLE NOTE		TWO HALF NOTES		FOUR QUARTER NOTES
4	EQUALS	**2/2**	OR	**1 1 / 1 1**
o		♩ ♩		♩ ♩ ♩ ♩

The WHOLE NOTE	The HALF NOTE	The QUARTER NOTE
receives 4 BEATS (4 counts).	receives 2 BEATS.	receives 1 BEAT.

Music is divided into equal parts called MEASURES. A BAR LINE divides one measure from another.

BAR LINE   BAR LINE   double bar line means the end.

| ONE MEASURE | ONE MEASURE |

To indicate the number of beats in each measure, we use a . . .

Time Signature

The TIME SIGNATURE **C** or **4/4** means

← four beats in each measure,

← a beat on each quarter note.

For each note value, there is a comparative REST sign.

◄ **NOTES**   **RESTS** ►

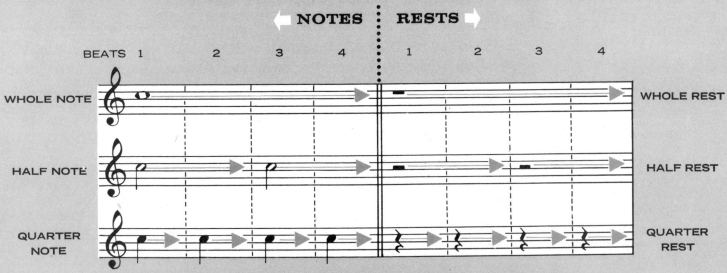

		NOTES				RESTS			
BEATS	1	2	3	4	1	2	3	4	
WHOLE NOTE									WHOLE REST
HALF NOTE									HALF REST
QUARTER NOTE									QUARTER REST

3

How To Tune Your Guitar

The six strings of your guitar are the same pitch as the six notes shown on the piano in the following illustration:

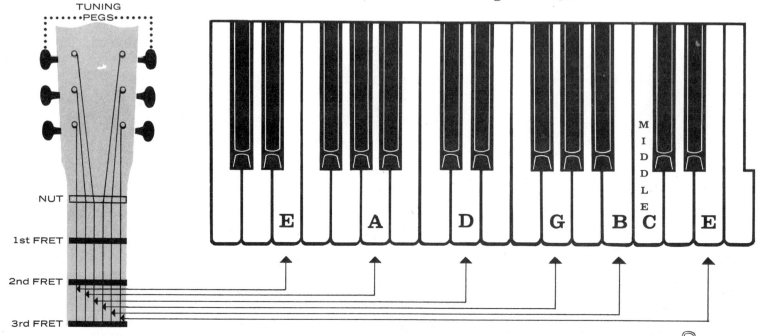

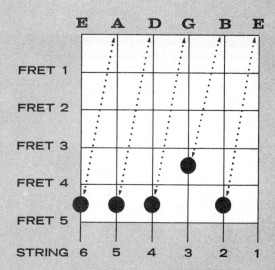

LEFT HAND FINGERING

Other Ways Of Tuning Your Guitar

Tune the 6th string to E on the piano. If no piano is available, approximate E as best you can and proceed as follows:

Press 5th fret of 6th string to get pitch of 5th string (A).
Press 5th fret of 5th string to get pitch of 4th string (D).
Press 5th fret of 4th string to get pitch of 3rd string (G).
Press 4th fret of 3rd string to get pitch of 2nd string (B).
Press 5th fret of 2nd string to get pitch of 1st string (E).

The 'Tune-Rite' record ($1) offers another easy solution to tuning. It allows the hands to be free while insuring perfect tuning by using a guitar sound on the record. Recorded by Alfred Music Co., this record may be ordered through your local music store.

Guitar Diagrams

When introducing the single notes of the guitar, two diagrams are used. One diagram is used to show the correct finger position of the note on the guitar fingerboard along with its musical notation. The other diagram is a review of all the notes introduced on that page and also includes the correct fingering for each note.

Notes on the First String (E)

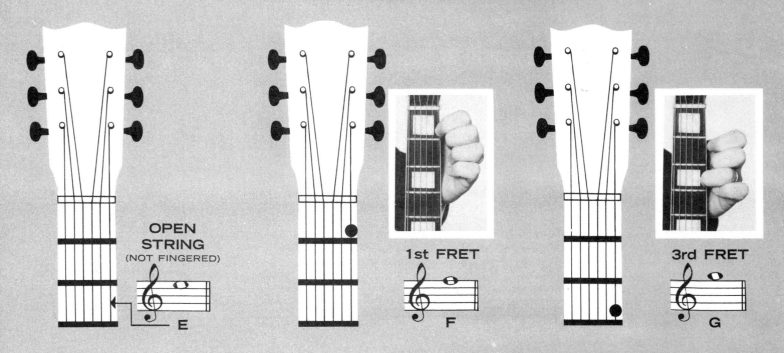

OPEN STRING (NOT FINGERED) — E

1st FRET — F

3rd FRET — G

Use only the down-stroke indicated by ⊓

		E	
FRET 1	F		1
FRET 2			
FRET 3	G		3

PLAY SLOWLY AND EVENLY

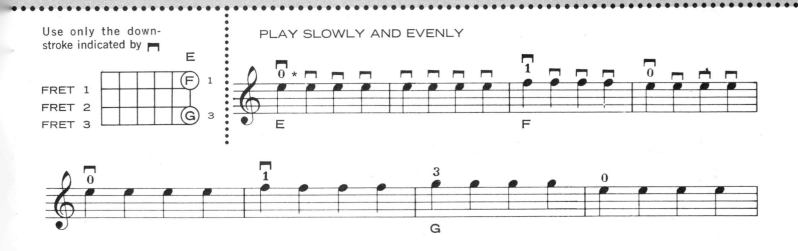

AND AWAY WE GO

DOUBLE BAR LINE

USED AT THE END OF A PIECE

*Use open string

MORE

STILL MORE

NO MORE

6

SOUND-OFF
(HOW TO COUNT TIME)

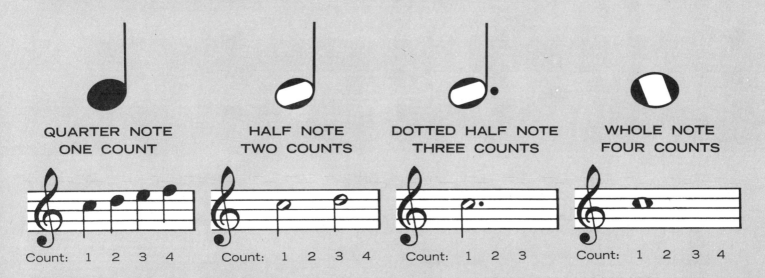

| QUARTER NOTE ONE COUNT | HALF NOTE TWO COUNTS | DOTTED HALF NOTE THREE COUNTS | WHOLE NOTE FOUR COUNTS |

Count: 1 2 3 4   Count: 1 2 3 4   Count: 1 2 3   Count: 1 2 3 4

Time Signatures

EACH PIECE OF MUSIC SHOULD HAVE NUMBERS AT THE BEGINNING, CALLED A TIME SIGNATURE. THESE NUMBERS TELL US HOW TO COUNT TIME.

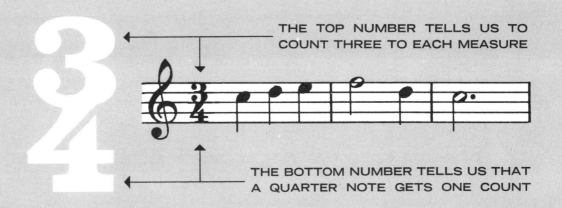

THE TOP NUMBER TELLS US TO COUNT THREE TO EACH MEASURE

THE BOTTOM NUMBER TELLS US THAT A QUARTER NOTE GETS ONE COUNT

FOUR COUNTS TO A MEASURE

A QUARTER NOTE GETS ONE COUNT

IMPORTANT!   FILL IN THE MISSING TIME SIGNATURES OF THE SONGS ALREADY LEARNED.

Notes on the Second String (B)

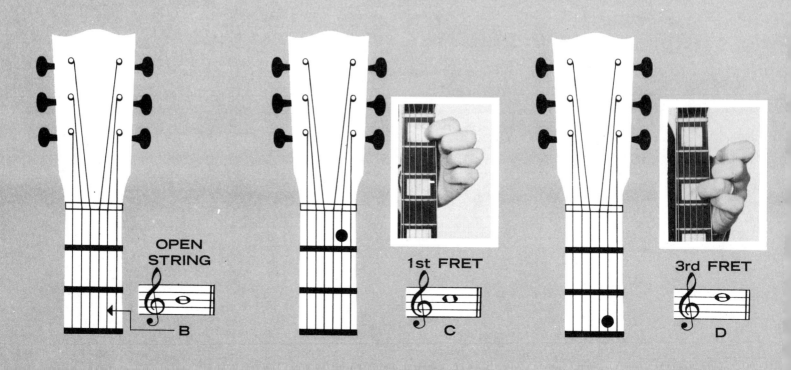

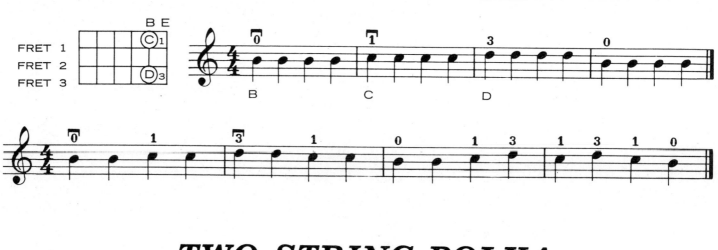

TWO-STRING POLKA

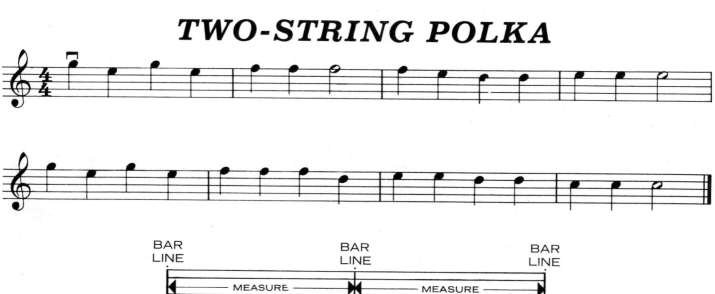

THE GREY GOOSE

BLUE BIRD WALTZ

JINGLE BELLS

*These letters are chords for the instructor who may use them as a 2nd part.

The Third String (G)

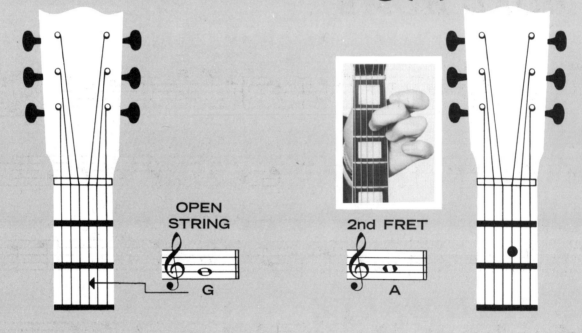

OPEN STRING — G

2nd FRET — A

TWO SOLOS ON THE THREE HIGHEST STRINGS

AU CLAIR DE LA LUNE

Use down-stroke only

These are _____ notes.

SHOO FLY

THE ROAD HOME

EAST SIDE, WEST SIDE

HOP-A-LONG

DANCE MARY, DANCE

ONE-TWO-THREE
HAWAIIAN SONG

MARGARITA

HOP, HOP, HOP

GEORGIA CAKE-WALK

HERE WE GO!

13

Notes on the Fourth String (D)

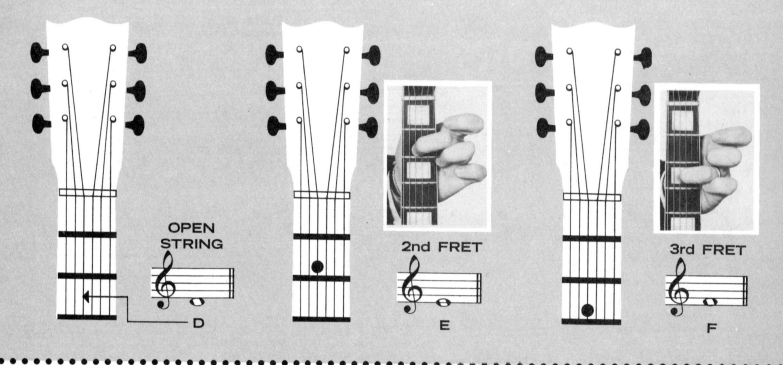

OPEN STRING — D   2nd FRET — E   3rd FRET — F

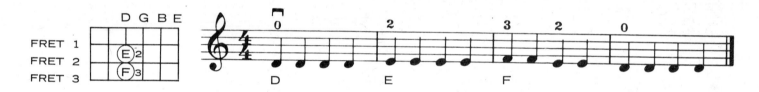

OLD MAC DONALD HAD A FARM

DOWN IN THE VALLEY

REUBEN REUBEN

COME TO THE SEA

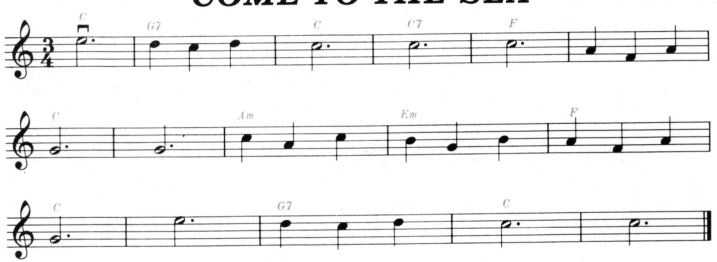

BOHEMIAN FOLK SONG

Introducing Chords

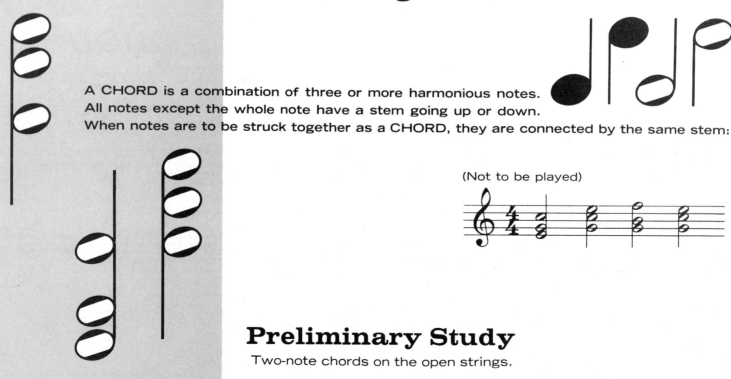

A CHORD is a combination of three or more harmonious notes.
All notes except the whole note have a stem going up or down.
When notes are to be struck together as a CHORD, they are connected by the same stem:

(Not to be played)

Preliminary Study

Two-note chords on the open strings.

Two-note chords with D as a bass note.

Use down-stroke only.

**LEARN THE ROTATION OF THE STRINGS THOROUGHLY.
PLAY WITH THE WRIST FREE AND RELAXED.
KEEP YOUR EYES ON THE NOTES.**

GOOD NIGHT, LADIES

NOBODY KNOWS THE TROUBLE I'VE SEEN

𝄴 means "common time" (the same as 4/4 time)

Review

Divide into measures

𝄴 means _____ counts per measure.   3/4 means _____ counts per measure.

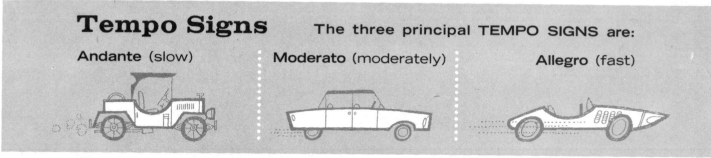

Tempo Signs

The three principal TEMPO SIGNS are:

Andante (slow) Moderato (moderately) Allegro (fast)

Three Note Chords

(On three open strings)

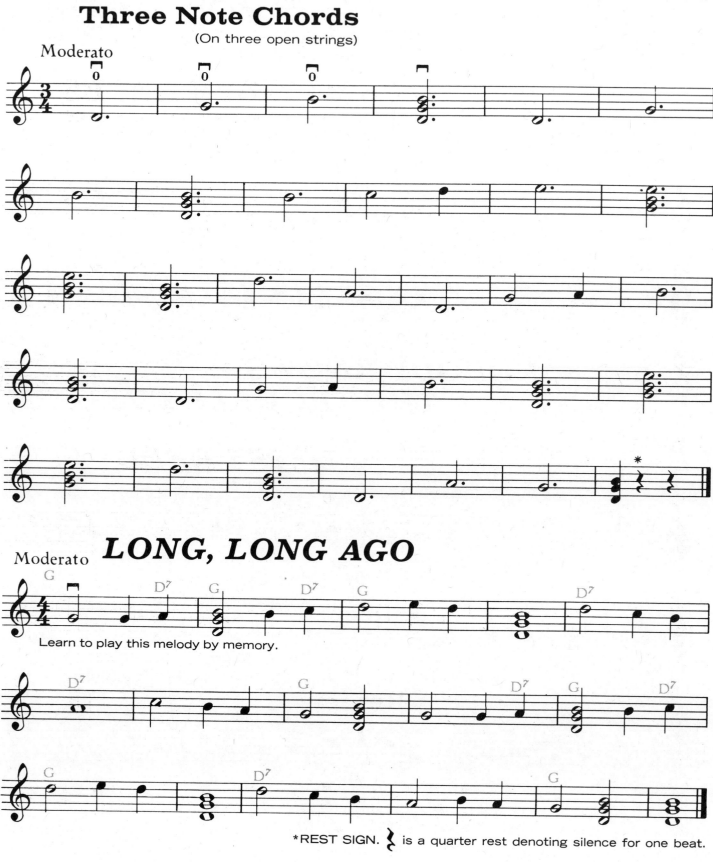

LONG, LONG AGO

Learn to play this melody by memory.

*REST SIGN. is a quarter rest denoting silence for one beat.

CAMPTOWN RACES

(Introducing chords with one note fingered)

DAISY BELL

The Fifth String (A)

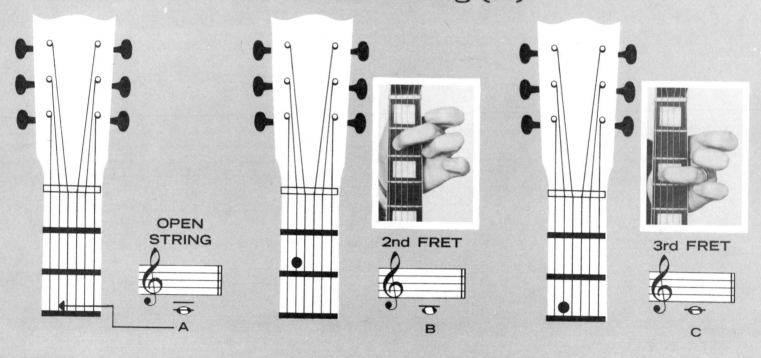

OPEN STRING — A
2nd FRET — B
3rd FRET — C

VOLGA BOATMAN

Andante

SKIP TO MY LOU

Allegro

The double dots inside the double bars indicate that everything between the double bars must be REPEATED.

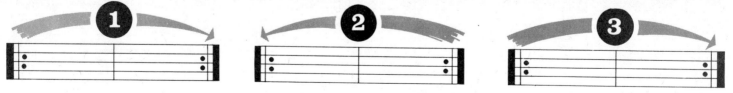

LAUGHING POLKA

Allegro

LIEBESTRAUM

Moderato

BUFFALO GALS

Allegro

Introducing High A

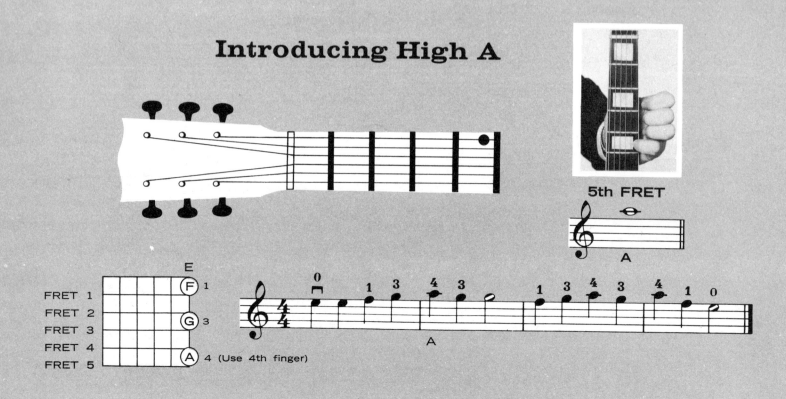

5th FRET

A

FRET 1					Ⓕ 1
FRET 2					
FRET 3					Ⓖ 3
FRET 4					
FRET 5					Ⓐ 4 (Use 4th finger)

E

A

BLUE TAIL FLY

Correct position of instrument is important!

THE LADY HAD A ROOSTER

Incomplete Measures

Every piece does not begin on the first beat. Music sometimes begins with an incomplete measure, called the UPBEAT, or PICK-UP. If the upbeat is one beat, the last measure will have only three beats in 4/4 , or 2 beats in 3/4 .

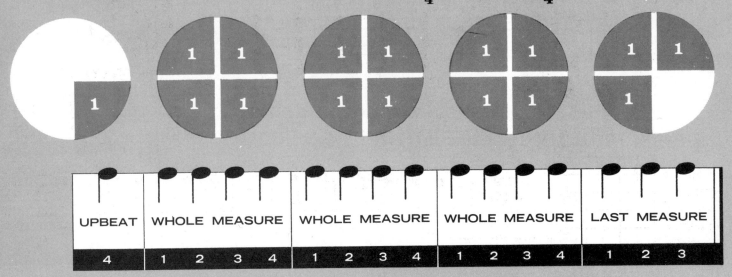

A-TISKIT, A-TASKIT

Moderato

THE YELLOW ROSE OF TEXAS

Allegro

* 𝄐 HOLD SIGN (Fermata): This sign indicates that the time value of the note is lengthened (approximately twice its usual value).

The Sixth String (E)

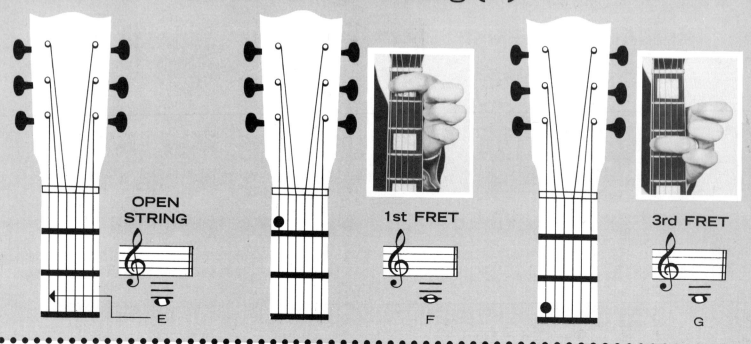

OPEN STRING — E
1st FRET — F
3rd FRET — G

Is your guitar in tune?

Using half and quarter notes, write notes studied. Mark letter name above each note.

The Natural Scale

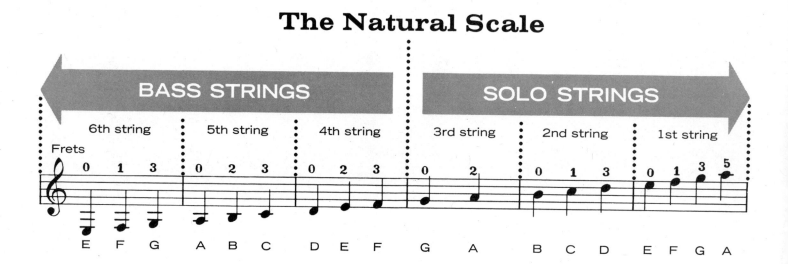

BASS STRINGS — SOLO STRINGS

6th string | 5th string | 4th string | 3rd string | 2nd string | 1st string

E F G | A B C | D E F | G A | B C D | E F G A

I'M A-LEAVIN' CHEYENNE

LIGHTLY ROW

THE BLUE DANUBE WALTZ

CAN-CAN DUET*

Allegro

J. OFFENBACH

*The 1st and 2nd part is to be played by the student. The teacher may accompany the student by playing the 2nd part, and vice versa. Follow this procedure on subsequent duets unless otherwise indicated.

The Dynamics

The signs showing how SOFT or LOUD to play the music are called the DYNAMICS. The principal dynamics are:

ECHO WALTZ

THE DESERT SONG
(STUDY IN COUNTING)

ON TOP OF OLD SMOKY

*A curved line ⌒ joining two notes on the same line or space is called a TIE.
The value of the second note is tied to the first. Do not strike the second note.

CARRY ME BACK TO OLD VIRGINNY

Andante

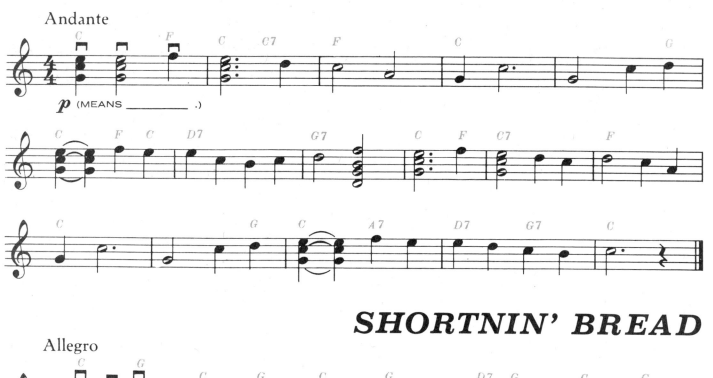

p (MEANS _____ .)

SHORTNIN' BREAD

Allegro

mf (MEANS _____ .)

SEA CHANTEY

Allegro

f (MEANS _____ .)

CHIAPANECAS
Mexican Hand-Clapping Song

Eighth Notes

Eighth notes are the black notes with a flag added to the stem ♪ or ♩. Two or more eighth notes are written ♫ or ♫. The 8th rest ♩.

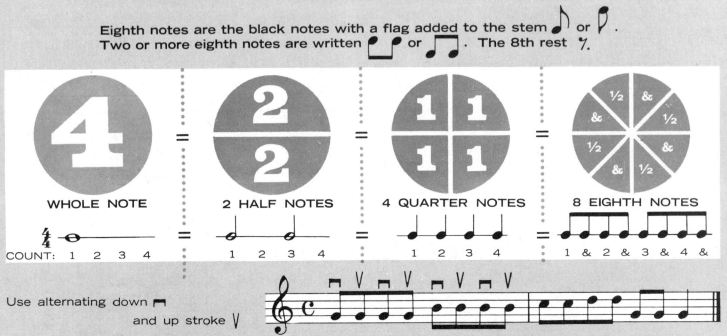

Use alternating down ⊓ and up stroke ∨

POLLY WOLLY DOODLE

SHE'LL BE COMIN' ROUND THE MOUNTAIN

*²⁄₄ — Two beats to a measure, a quarter note receives one beat.

32

THE BIG CORRAL

Speed Drill No. 1

Speed drills are for the development of technic and should be practised daily. Start all speed drills slowly and be sure that each note is clear and distinct. On each repetition increase the tempo.

BURY ME NOT ON THE LONE PRAIRIE

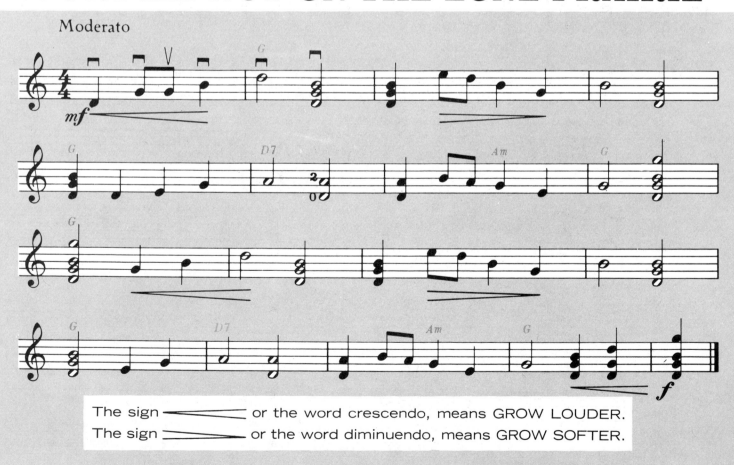

The sign ———— or the word crescendo, means GROW LOUDER.
The sign ———— or the word diminuendo, means GROW SOFTER.

DRINK TO ME ONLY WITH THINE EYES

ALTERNATING MELODY AND ACCOMPANIMENT IN THE KEY OF C

35

♯ Sharps, ♭ Flats, and ♮ Naturals

The distance from one fret to the next fret, up or down, is a HALF STEP. TWO half steps make a WHOLE STEP.

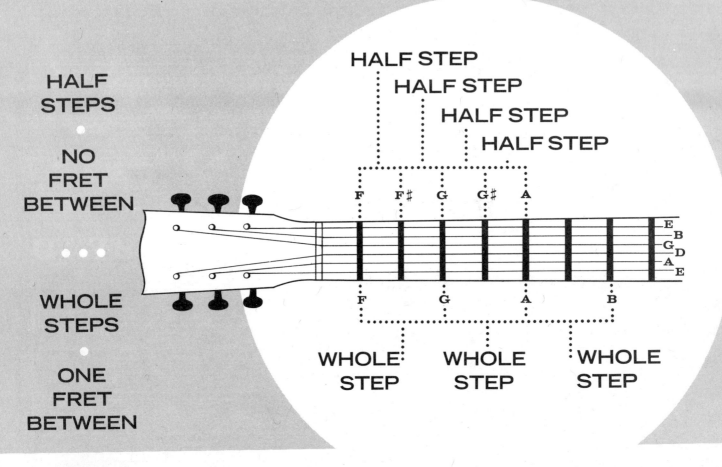

HALF STEPS
•
NO FRET BETWEEN

WHOLE STEPS
•
ONE FRET BETWEEN

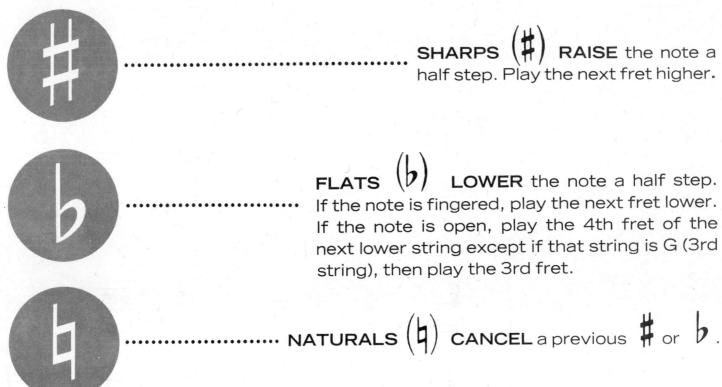

SHARPS (♯) **RAISE** the note a half step. Play the next fret higher.

FLATS (♭) **LOWER** the note a half step. If the note is fingered, play the next fret lower. If the note is open, play the 4th fret of the next lower string except if that string is G (3rd string), then play the 3rd fret.

NATURALS (♮) **CANCEL** a previous ♯ or ♭.

The Chromatic Scale

The CHROMATIC SCALE is formed exclusively of HALF STEPS.

Ascending, the CHROMATIC SCALE uses SHARPS, (♯),

the descending scale uses FLATS, (♭).

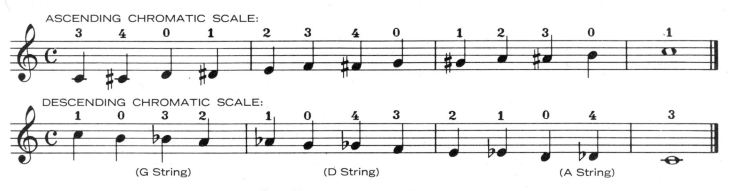

CHROMATIC WALTZ

Moderato

HEAR ME LITTLE ONE

Allegro

COUNTY FAIR

Moderato

Speed Drill No. 2

Start slowly, then increase tempo on each repetition.

LA CUCARACHA

Moderato

LEARN BOTH PARTS! The solo part gives you practice in repeated notes. The 2nd part is further study in chord accompaniment in C.

The Major Scale

A scale is a succession of eight tones in alphabetical order. All major scales are built in the same form:

**WHOLE STEP, WHOLE STEP, HALF STEP,
WHOLE STEP, WHOLE STEP, WHOLE STEP, HALF STEP.**

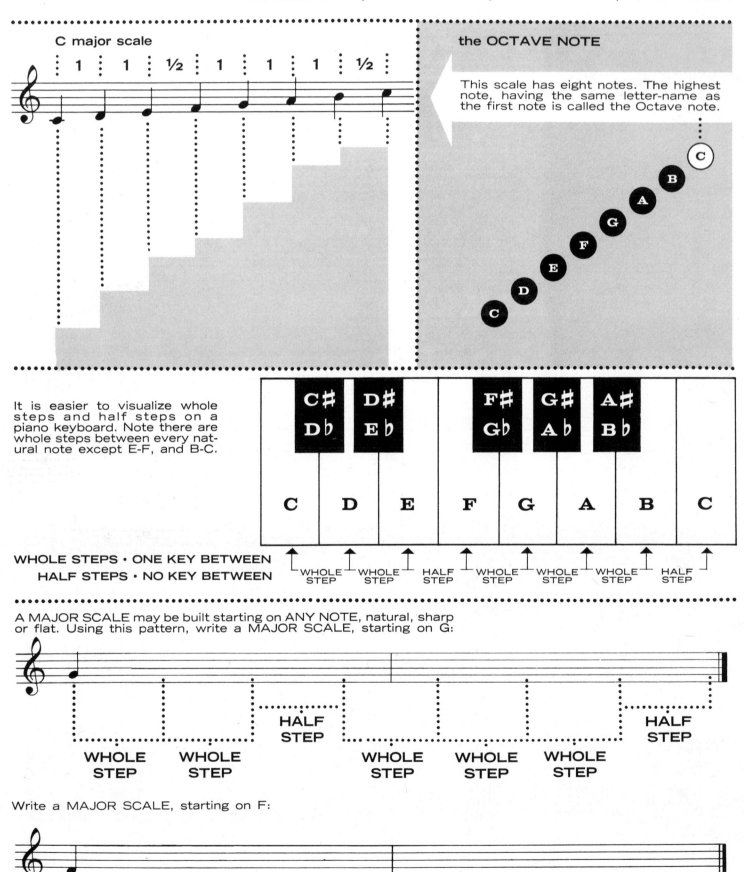

C major scale

the OCTAVE NOTE

This scale has eight notes. The highest note, having the same letter-name as the first note is called the Octave note.

It is easier to visualize whole steps and half steps on a piano keyboard. Note there are whole steps between every natural note except E-F, and B-C.

WHOLE STEPS · ONE KEY BETWEEN

HALF STEPS · NO KEY BETWEEN

A MAJOR SCALE may be built starting on ANY NOTE, natural, sharp or flat. Using this pattern, write a MAJOR SCALE, starting on G:

WHOLE STEP · WHOLE STEP · HALF STEP · WHOLE STEP · WHOLE STEP · WHOLE STEP · HALF STEP

Write a MAJOR SCALE, starting on F:

CHECK: Are the notes in alphabetical order?

Key Signatures

The Key of C MAJOR:

A piece based on the C MAJOR SCALE is in the KEY OF C MAJOR. Since there are no sharps or flats in the C scale, any sharps or flats occurring in a piece in the KEY OF C MAJOR are called ACCIDENTALS.

The Key of G MAJOR:

A piece based on the G MAJOR SCALE is in the KEY OF G MAJOR. Since F is sharp in the G scale, every F will be sharp in the key of G major. Instead of making all the F's sharp in the piece, the sharp is indicated at the beginning, in the KEY SIGNATURE. Sharps or flats shown in the KEY SIGNATURE are effective throughout the piece.

Key Signature:
One Sharp (F#)

The Key of F MAJOR:

A piece based on the F MAJOR SCALE is in the KEY OF F MAJOR.

The key signature is ONE FLAT (B♭).

If sharps, flats or naturals not shown in the key signature occur in the piece, they are called ACCIDENTALS. ACCIDENTALS are effective only for the measures in which they appear.

The three scales shown above should be practiced every day. Students who do this should have little difficulty playing selections written in C MAJOR, G MAJOR and F MAJOR.

Three Melodies in Three Keys

BIRTHDAY SONG

FRÈRE JACQUES
ROUND

BILL GROGAN'S GOAT

TINKER POLKA

Introducing Dotted Quarter Notes

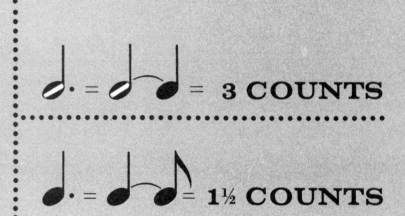

A DOT ... increases the length of a note ONE-HALF!

♩. = ♩ ♩ = 3 COUNTS

♩. = ♩ ♪ = 1½ COUNTS

Preparatory Drill:

(REPEAT)

(TIE)

The only difference in the following three measures and those directly above them is the way they are written. They should sound the SAME.

COUNT: 1 & 2 & 3 4

AULD LANG SYNE

Allegro

MARCH OF THE THREE KINGS

SANTA LUCIA

AMERICA

THE SPANISH CAVALIER

MARCH SONG from "The Chimes of Normandy"

APACHE WAR DANCE

SHEPHERD'S HEY

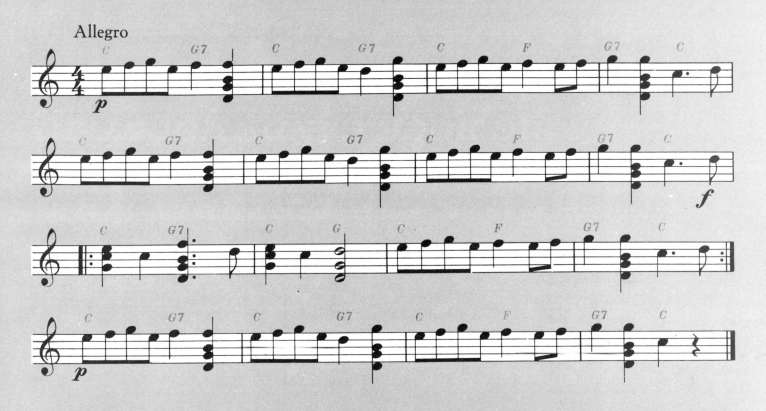

HAIL! HAIL! THE GANG'S ALL HERE

OUR BOYS

Certificate of Promotion

This certifies that

_____

has mastered and perfected
Book 1 of ALFRED'S BASIC GUITAR COURSE
and is hereby promoted into
Book 2 of ALFRED'S BASIC GUITAR COURSE

Teacher _____

Date _____